super juicer

super juicer

a collection of health-enhancing juices that replenish, restore, and revitalize

Christine France

This edition published in 2009
Love Food ℗ is an imprint of Parragon Books Ltd

Parragon
Queen Street House
4 Queen Street
Bath BA1 1HE, UK

Copyright © Parragon Books Ltd 2007

Love Food ® and the accompanying heart device is a trademark of Parragon Books Ltd

Internal design by Talking Design
Cover design by Sarah Edwards
Photography by Clive Streeter
Food styling by Angela Drake
Introduction and recipes written by Christine France
Edited by Fiona Biggs

ISBN 978-1-4075-7869-9

Printed in Indonesia

NOTES FOR THE READER
This book uses imperial, metric, and U.S. cup measurements. Follow the same units of measurement throughout; do not mix imperial and metric. All spoon measurements are level: teaspoons are assumed to be 5 ml, and tablespoons are assumed to be 15 ml. Unless otherwise stated, milk is assumed to be lowfat, eggs and individual vegetables such as potatoes are medium, and pepper is freshly ground black pepper. Sufferers from liver disease and those with weakened immune systems should never eat raw fish. Likewise, pregnant women, nursing mothers, and young children should avoid eating raw fish, especially larger species such as swordfish and tuna, which tend to have high concentrations of mercury. Recipes using raw or very lightly cooked eggs should be avoided by infants, the elderly, pregnant women, convalescents, and anyone with a chronic condition. The times given are an approximate guide only. Preparation times differ according to the techniques used by different people and the cooking times may also vary from those given. Optional ingredients, variations or serving suggestions have not been included in the calculations.

contents

introduction

If you're new to juicing, then you have a real treat in store. Not only are the health benefits of freshly extracted juices unbelievably good, but you'll be surprised how wonderful the flavors can be. Even foods you never believed you would enjoy are suddenly transformed into succulent, rich-tasting super juices in a matter of seconds.

Juicing Equipment

There are basically three types of juicer: centrifugal, masticating, and press. The majority of modern domestic juicers work on the centrifugal force method—the fruit is ground against blades to break it up, while spinning at high speed to force out the juice through a fine mesh. This is the type we have designed the recipes in this book for. It's as simple as popping in the fruit or vegetables, switching on, and catching the juice that comes out in a matter of seconds.

Purchasing Pointers

- It's worth buying the best quality juicer you can afford, particularly if you plan to juice often or in large amounts. As always, you get what you pay for and, what price can you put on good health?
- A compact, well-designed machine takes up as little space as possible on your counter and looks good, too.
- A powerful motor is essential to make juices efficiently and quickly.
- Check noise levels, as juicers vary and some can be very loud—if you plan to juice early in the morning, it could be a rather sharp wake-up!
- Variable speed is useful if you are juicing a variety of different ingredients—for example high speed for apples and carrots, low speed for mangoes and grapes.
- Insure the juicer is easy to clean, with simple, unfussy parts that come apart easily.
- Check that the juicer has nonslip feet to keep it in place on the counter.
- Most juicers now have a safety-lock lid, and it's worth testing this before buying.

Additional Kit

- Handheld blender—turns juices into smoothies; some ingredients such as bananas or avocados are not suitable for juicing but do add very valuable fiber and nutrients. A freestanding, pitcher-type blender also makes smoothies, but is more bulky.
- Measuring pitchers—most juicers provide one, but you may find a spare one useful, too.
- Small whisk—for combining juices that tend to settle and separate quickly.

- Sharp knives—if produce has to be cut, use the sharpest knife possible to avoid unnecessary vitamin loss.

Advantages of Home Juicing

So, why don't we just buy readymade juices from the supermarket? Well, there's nothing wrong with store-bought juices, it's just that there's really no comparison—homemade juices are better in so many ways:

- Unless you buy freshly-made juice from a juice bar, store-bought juices will have lost valuable nutrients during storage. Juices made at home can be absolutely fresh and consumed immediately, retaining maximum amounts of nutrients, and more flavor.
- Store-bought juices have usually been heat-treated or have additives to help them keep longer. Fruit "drinks" are not entirely made from juice—they can be made from concentrates mixed with water.
- If you make your own juices, you're not buying

expensive and wasteful packaging.
- Juicing at home need not be expensive if you buy ingredients when they're in season and look for bargains in your local stores.
- Home juicing is fun—you can create different combinations that will never be available in the shops. Experiment and make your own concoctions to suit your own taste, or to help a particular health condition.

...and the Disadvantages?

- Juicers can be bulky, so make sure you have enough space in your kitchen to keep your juicer out on the counter all the time; it's unlikely that it will be used regularly if it's stored in a cupboard—out of sight is out of mind!
- Even well-designed juicers are not easy to wash up. The filter should never be allowed to dry with food deposits on it. Just put it in a bowl of hot soapy water before the pulp dries, and the rest is relatively easy. Most parts can be put in the dishwasher (although you should consult the manufacturer's handbook before doing this).

Uses for Pulp

The pulp left behind after juicing still contains valuable fiber and nutrients, so you shouldn't waste it:

- Add to cakes and bakes—for example carrot cake, fruit cake, cookies, and muffins.
- Stir into soups and casseroles to thicken, or add to ground meat mixtures for burgers or Bolognese sauce.
- Add to the compost—as pulp is already partially broken down it accelerates the composting process.

Nutritional Benefits of Juicing

We all know that we should be eating a minimum of five portions of fruit and vegetables each day, but it's not always easy. Juicing is just one more way to get your fruit and vegetable counts up, and add life-enhancing nutrients to your diet in an easily absorbed form. Regular juicing helps increase vitality, boost energy levels, and fight disease.

Just 5 fl oz/150 ml of juice counts as one of your five-a-day portions, but remember that juice cannot count for more than one portion as it does not contain all the nutrients you get from whole fruit and vegetables.

The fiber in fruit and vegetables contains beneficial nutrients—because juicing breaks up these fibers, it allows them to be available to the body in an easily digestible form. The enzymes released actually help the body to absorb vital vitamins and minerals.

Basic Nutrition

No single food can provide all the nutrition we need to stay healthy, so you should aim to eat a wide variety of different foods to obtain all the necessary nutrients.

• Carbohydrate

Carbohydrate is a form of fuel, which the body uses to make energy. There are basically two types of carbohydrate: fast-release or "simple" carbohydrates, and slow-release, "complex," or starchy carbohydrates.

Simple carbohydrates, found in sugar and honey, should be eaten only in limited amounts as excessive quantities can cause health problems such as diabetes, obesity, heart disease, and cancer. Complex carbohydrates, found mainly in whole grains, pulses, vegetables, and fruits, should make up about two thirds of your diet.

• **Fat**

The body uses fats to make energy. There are two main types: saturated fat, usually solid at room temperature, is mainly found in meat and dairy products and processed foods. A diet rich in saturated fat can lead to heart disease and obesity.

Unsaturated fats are usually liquid at room temperature. These are polyunsaturated, including the Omega 3 and Omega 6 oils found in oily fish, nuts, and seeds, and monounsaturated, found in olive oil and canola oil. These essential oils are linked to healthy brain function, reduced risk of heart disease, and lower cholesterol levels.

It's recommended that around two thirds of our fat intake should be polyunsaturated and no more than a third should be saturated.

• **Protein**

Our bodies need protein for growth and cell repair. The main sources are meat, fish, eggs, and soybeans, which contain all the amino acids we need. Vegetables, particularly pulses, are also a good source if you eat a wide variety, and these contribute complex carbohydrates, which meat sources don't have, to the diet.

Most of us eat too much protein—for instance, an adult female needs just $1^1/_2$ oz/45 g per day, and an adult male just 2 oz/55 g per day.

• **Fiber**

Although we cannot digest fiber, it is essential for keeping the bowels healthy and allows other nutrients to be absorbed.

Fiber is divided into two groups, soluble and insoluble, both found in whole grain cereals, pulses, fruits, and vegetables. Soluble fiber can help to reduce levels of cholesterol in the blood and regulate blood sugar levels. Insoluble fiber helps prevent constipation and may prevent bowel cancer.

Healthy eating guidelines recommend that we should eat around $3/_4$ oz/18 g of fiber per day.

• **Vitamins**

Vitamins are organic substances that are essential for general good health and tissue repair, and also help the body to release the energy from carbohydrates. Each vitamin has specific uses in the body—vitamin A, for instance, is needed for healthy growth, good skin and vision, and a healthy immune system.

Some vitamins can be stored in the body (A, D, E, K, and B_{12}) but others must be consumed regularly to maintain healthy levels. Water-soluble vitamins (B complex and C) are easily destroyed during processing, storage, and cooking. Fat-soluble vitamins (A, D, E, and K) are more stable.

Juicing is a good way to make sure we consume a wide variety of vitamin-rich foods every day.

• **Minerals**

Minerals are inorganic substances that perform many functions in keeping our bodies healthy. Only about 20 minerals are thought to be essential and need to be obtained from foods.

Some minerals, such as potassium, which helps maintain healthy nerves, blood pressure, and fluid levels in the body, are needed in relatively large amounts. Others, such as selenium, a powerful antioxidant which can protect against heart disease, are needed in such small quantities that they are known as "trace elements."

Super Foods

All foods have some nutritional value, but some foods are more nutrient-packed than others. Here are some of the very best foods to include in your juice drinks:

Apples—rich in antioxidants, vitamin C for healthy skin, and soluble fiber to reduce blood cholesterol. Contain quercetin, a phytonutrient that may help fight cancer.

Avocados—very energy-rich, and a good source of vitamin E, which repairs tissues, lowers blood pressure, and reduces cholesterol. Use in smoothies.

Bananas—very energy-rich, high in fiber, and a good source of potassium, which regulates blood pressure. Use in smoothies.

Beets—rich in potassium, iron, and folic acid, so good for the blood and arteries. The leafy tops are rich in beta-carotene, an antioxidant that the body converts to vitamin A.

Blueberries—the top antioxidant fruit boosts the immune system, helps fight conditions associated with aging, such as Alzheimer's disease, protects eyesight, and destroys free radicals linked with cancer.

Broccoli—rich in cancer-fighting phytochemicals, with vitamins A and C, folic acid, which help prevent birth defects, and potassium, which helps regulate blood pressure.

Ginger—a natural antibiotic that helps digestion and stimulates the circulation.

Nuts and seeds—a great source of protein and the essential oils, Omega 3 and 6, plus protein, vitamins, and minerals. Flax seeds are rich in phytoestrogens, which can regulate female hormones.

Onions and garlic—the allium family has antibacterial and antifungal compounds, and phytochemicals that fight cancer and heart disease and help the liver eliminate toxins from the body.

Oranges—a good source of vitamins A, C, B_6, beta-carotene, and folic acid. Citrus fruits are high in lutein, a carotenoid that helps reduce the risk of colon cancer.

Soymilk and soy yogurt—are rich in powerful isoflavones, which fight cancer, reduce cholesterol, and relieve menopausal symptoms.

Spinach—dark green leafy vegetables are rich in B vitamins, particularly folates, essential for normal tissue growth, and are particularly useful during pregnancy. Spinach contains more protein than most vegetables.

Tomatoes—a great source of lycopene, a phytochemical that has cancer-fighting properties and helps protect against heart disease. One large tomato provides 40 percent of our daily requirement of vitamin C.

Preparing for Juicing

Buying the right produce and storing and preparing it well is critical to the amount of juicy nutrients you'll get:

- Use organic produce, if possible, then you can use the whole fruit or vegetable without worrying about pesticide and herbicide residues.
- Always wash fresh produce, scrubbing with a soft brush if necessary. If not organic, wash in water with a little washing-up liquid, then rinse thoroughly.
- To get maximum nutritive value from fresh produce, it's best to juice ingredients whole. Most modern juicers have large feed tubes to allow for this. So, unless it's necessary to chop items to get them into the juicer, leave them whole, with skins and cores. Bitter or waxy peel and large pits should be removed to avoid damaging the juicer.
- Use really fresh produce that's at its peak, and don't be tempted to buy bruised or damaged overripe fruit and vegetables, which will have lost food value and flavor.
- Store most vegetables in a cool, airy place, and salads in the crisper compartment of the refrigerator, but use them all quickly before nutrients are lost. Soft, berry-type fruits can be stored in the refrigerator but need to be used quickly for maximum food value. Fruits such as apples, pears, tropical fruits, and citrus fruits are best stored at cool room temperature as they give up more juice.
- Wash produce before storage, if possible, so that it's ready for juicing at any time.

Juicing for Children

- Juices are a great way to encourage fussy eaters. Children often find the idea of colorful juices more exciting than a plate of vegetables. In addition, it's easy to sneak in a carrot when you're juicing oranges.
- Adding an apple or pear to a vegetable juice can make it more palatable for children.
- Juices should be diluted for children, with mineral water or lemonade.
- Young children love to watch juices being made and often enjoy helping to prepare, but for safety's sake don't allow them to use the juicer themselves.

- Do make sure that children (and adults, too!) brush their teeth after drinking fresh juices, as even natural sugars can cause tooth decay.

Does Juicing Cost a Fortune?

The short answer is no, as long as you shop sensibly:

- Use produce that's at the peak of its season, when it's not only cheaper but also has the finest flavor and maximum nutrients.
- Look out for special offers and bulk-buys in fruit and vegetables. Many suppliers will sell a whole tray or box of produce for a cheaper price.
- Avoid over-packaged produce and buy loose if possible, which is cheaper and more environmentally friendly.
- Combine some of your purchasing with a friend or neighbor who also has a juicer, to bulk buy and save money.
- If you buy more produce than you need at one time, freeze some for later, or make a larger batch of juice and freeze that for later use, in portion-sized amounts for easy thawing.
- Be creative with your juicing. Just check out the fridge or fruit bowl and have a go—you'll soon find that there's no need for anything to go to waste.
- When you have a glut in the vegetable garden, it's time to start juicing; make the most of homegrown produce as it's cheaper and more organic than buying.

Safety Notes

- If you are taking medication, consult your doctor before consuming grapefruit juice, as this can inhibit some medications.
- If you're adding supplements or herbal additives, for example spirulina or ginseng, read the manufacturer's instructions for dosage, and, if in doubt, check with your doctor.
- If you're new to juicing, start with no more than two juices per day, to give your body a chance to adjust.

vitality-boosting

01

The moment you wake up in the morning is the best time of day to drink fresh juice, as that's when your body is most able to absorb those wonderful vitamins and minerals. Resist the temptation to make juice the night before—you'll lose some of the goodness and there's nothing better than really fresh juice.

serves 1–2

1 ripe mango
1 orange
1/2 pomegranate

tropical sunrise

This beautifully colored juice is packed with powerful heart-protective and cancer-fighting antioxidants, plus vitamins B and C. Mangoes, oranges, and pomegranate seeds are all good sources of potassium, which helps to regulate blood pressure.

Remove the pit from the mango, and peel the orange. Juice them together and pour into glasses. Peel the pomegranate, reserve 1 tablespoon of the seeds, and juice the rest. Pour into the orange and mango juice and sprinkle with the reserved pomegranate seeds.

serves 1–2

3$\frac{1}{2}$ fl oz/100 ml boiling
  water
1 green tea sachet,
  or 1 tsp green tea
1 carrot
1 apple
small handful flat-leaf
  parsley
sprigs of flat-leaf parsley,
  to garnish

bright eyes

The carrots and parsley in this juice are packed with carotenoids to brighten the eyes and skin and help cleanse the liver. It's also full of antioxidants, which regulate blood pressure, lower cholesterol, and fight heart disease and cancer.

Pour the boiling water onto the green tea and let stand for 4 minutes. Strain and cool slightly. Juice the carrot, apple, and parsley. Stir the juice into the tea, pour into glasses, and serve warm or cold, garnished with parsley sprigs.

serves 1–2

$^1\!/_2$ peach
1 small apple
$^1\!/_2$ kiwi fruit
2 oz/55 g green grapes
7 oz/200 g honeydew
  melon flesh
slice of kiwi,
  to garnish

fruity refresher

Rich in vitamin C and beta-carotene, this is an excellent cleanser, diuretic, and energizer to liven up a sluggish system in the mornings. Melon cleanses the intestines, bladder, and kidneys and clears the skin. Grape skins contain tannins that help to stimulate the appetite.

Halve and pit the peach. Juice the peach, apple, and kiwi fruit, then add the grapes and melon. Stir the juice, pour into glasses, and serve, garnished with the slice of kiwi.

serves 1–2

2 small beets
1 carrot
1 pear
$\frac{1}{2}$ lime
1-inch/2.5-cm piece of
  fresh ginger

red reviver

Beets are very rich in potassium, which is highly effective in keeping blood pressure low. Rich in vitamins and antioxidants, the Red Reviver protects against aging free radicals and helps normal cell function. Ginger is a good wake-up, as it stimulates circulation and peps up the digestion.

Juice the beets and carrot, then juice the pear, lime, and ginger. Mix together, pour into glasses, and serve.

serves 1–2

1 pomegranate
$^1/_2$ small orange
4 passion fruit
$3^1/_2$–$4^1/_2$ fl oz/100–125 ml
   sparkling mineral water

passionate juice fizz

This delicate pink drink is powerfully rich in antioxidants, calcium, vitamin C, and vitamin E, phytochemicals that protect the heart, and enzymes that are good for the digestive system. Mineral water speeds up the absorption of the nutrients.

Peel the rind from the pomegranate and peel the orange, leaving on the white pith. Scoop the flesh from the passion fruit. Juice the pomegranate with the orange and pulp from 3 passion fruit. Pour into a glass and stir in the remaining passion fruit pulp. Top up with the mineral water and serve.

serves 1–2

1 orange
large sprig of fresh mint
7 oz/200 g cantaloupe
  melon flesh
sprigs of mint, to
  decorate

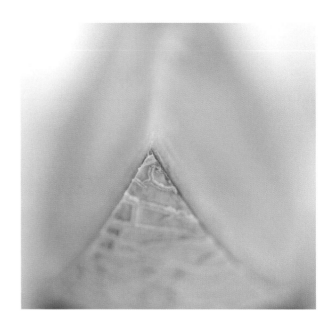

wake-up juice

A light and refreshing drink for a fresh start after a late night, packed with vitamin C. Melon juice is diuretic and rich in healing beta-carotene. The aromatic oils in mint aid and soothe the digestion and help to calm the nerves, while at the same time freshening the breath.

Peel the orange, leaving on the white pith. Juice the orange, mint, and melon. Pour into glasses and serve, decorated with sprigs of mint.

serves 1–2

1 pink grapefruit
1 orange
$^1/_2$ lemon
$^1/_2$ lime
slice of lime, to decorate

pink zinger

Packed with vitamin C, which soaks up the free radicals that cause aging, the Pink Zinger helps with healing and strengthening the body's resistance to infections. It's an energizing start to the day that flushes toxins from the intestines for clear skin and a healthy system.

Peel the grapefruit, orange, lemon, and lime, leaving on the white pith. Juice the grapefruit, orange, lemon, and lime together. Pour into a glass and serve with a slice of lime on the rim of the glass.

serves 1–2

1 ruby grapefruit, peeled
5 oz/140 g raspberries
2 oz/55 g cranberries

rosy glow

A vibrant ruby-colored juice, rich in beta-carotene, antioxidants, and bioflavonoids which help absorption of vitamin C. Cranberry helps with bladder problems and can cure cystitis.

Cut the grapefruit into quarters, then pack half into the juicer. Top with the raspberries and cranberries, then add the remaining grapefruit. Juice all the fruit together. Pour into glasses and serve immediately.

serves 1–2

7 oz/200 g strawberries
3¹/2 oz/100 g raspberries
3¹/2 fl oz/100 ml soymilk
1¹/2 oz/40 g unsweetened
  granola

breakfast berry smoothie

This breakfast-in-a-glass is packed with sustaining nutrients to keep up your energy levels all morning. Strawberries contain lignin, which helps reduce blood cholesterol, and oats are one of the most effective cholesterol-lowering foods.

Reserve a strawberry for decoration, then juice the remainder with the raspberries. Place the juice in a blender with the soymilk and granola, and blend until almost smooth. Pour into glasses, top each smoothie with half a strawberry, and serve.

serves 1–2

$1/2$ cucumber
2 apples
$1/2$ oz/15 g fresh cilantro,
   leaves and stems

cucumber cooler

Cucumber is high in water content so it's great for rehydrating and refreshing the system, and is a very good diuretic. Apples contain natural sugars for an energy lift. Cilantro promotes good digestion and can remove toxins. It also helps the circulation and is good for healthy eyesight.

Cut a few long strips from the cucumber and reserve. Juice the apples, cilantro, and cucumber together. Pour into glasses, add the cucumber strips, and serve.

empowering

02

When energy levels dip during a busy day, it's easy to reach for a quick sugar-fix or caffeine, but what you really need is longer-lasting energy to build and repair, for brain power and renewed strength. Invest in a flask to carry your juice to work, to the gym, or anywhere your busy life takes you, ready to refuel at any time of day.

serves 1–2

2 nectarines
3$^{1}/_{2}$ oz/100 g green
   seedless grapes
3$^{1}/_{2}$ oz/100 g soy yogurt
$^{1}/_{2}$ tsp honey, preferably
   Manuka
1 tbsp sunflower seeds

sunshine smoothie

A vitamin-packed, energizing smoothie that's a satisfying and healthy snack at any time of day. It's rich in vitamin A, which helps maintain a healthy skin and immune system.

Halve and pit the nectarines then juice with the grapes. Add to the yogurt, honey, and half the sunflower seeds and blend until smooth. Pour into a glass, sprinkle with the remaining sunflower seeds, and serve.

serves 1–2

12 oz/350 g dark sweet
  cherries
$^1/_2$ lime
1 apple
3$^1/_2$ oz/100 g red grapes
1$^1/_2$ oz/40 g soy yogurt

cherry pink

Naturally sweet and energy-rich, this juice is a perfect midday boost when you're working hard. It's high in vitamin C, cancer-fighting phytochemicals, antioxidants, and calcium for strength.

Pit the cherries. Halve the lime. Juice the apple, cherries, grapes, and lime together. Whisk in the yogurt, pour into glasses, and serve.

serves 1–2

2 apples
1 small banana
2 tbsp plain yogurt
1 tbsp light tahini
$^1/_2$ tsp sesame seeds, for
  sprinkling

banana velvet

This juice provides a good combination of natural sugars for instant energy and soluble fiber for slow-release energy, and is a good source of protein and calcium for building strong muscles and bones.

Juice the apples. Add the peeled banana, yogurt, and tahini. Blend until smooth and frothy. Pour into a glass, sprinkle with sesame seeds, and serve.

serves 1–2

1 small zucchini
1 celery stalk
1¹/₂ oz/40 g baby leaf
  spinach
1¹/₂ oz/40 g alfalfa
  sprouts
2 apples
1 tsp alfalfa sprouts,
  to garnish

rapid recharge

This is a treasure trove of B vitamins, iron, healing phytochemicals, calcium, and protein, plus fruit sugars for a quick energy boost. It regulates blood pressure, reduces fluid retention, and helps to strengthen tissues and bones.

Trim the zucchini and pack into the juicer with the celery, add the spinach and the alfalfa, then the apples. Juice all the ingredients, then pour into glasses. Garnish with a few alfalfa sprouts and serve.

serves 1–2

7 oz/200 g parsnips
3¹/₂ oz/100 g broccoli
  florets
3¹/₂ oz/100 g peas
large sprig of fresh mint
2 apples
paprika,
  for sprinkling

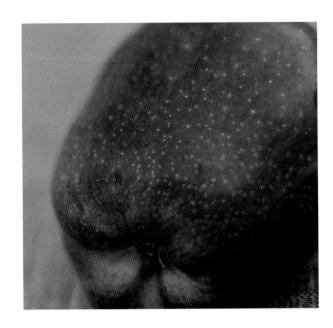

the protector

This delicate, pale green juice is great for all-round body maintenance, as it's very high in a good range of nutrients, including vitamins A, B, and C, protein, and iron. It's also rich in potassium, which helps normal cell function.

Pack the parsnips, broccoli, peas, mint, and apples into the juicer, then juice all the ingredients together. Pour into a glass and sprinkle with paprika to serve.

serves 1–2

1 pear
1¹/₂ oz/40 g young
  spinach
4 sprigs of parsley
¹/₄ cucumber
¹/₂ ripe Hass avocado
¹/₂ tsp spirulina powder
1 Brazil nut

avocado power pack

A super-smoothie, packed with antioxidants, vitamins, and minerals, including B vitamins, which regulate brain and nerve function. Spirulina contains the highest concentration of nutrients in any food and helps replenish the body's vital stores.

Pack the pear, spinach, parsley, and cucumber into the juicer and juice. Remove the pit and skin from the avocado and add to the juice. Blend until smooth, then pour into a glass.

Mix the spirulina powder with just enough water to make a thick liquid, then swirl into the juice. Roughly chop the Brazil nut and sprinkle over to serve.

serves 1–2

2 apples
1 banana
1 tbsp peanut butter
slices of apple, to
  decorate

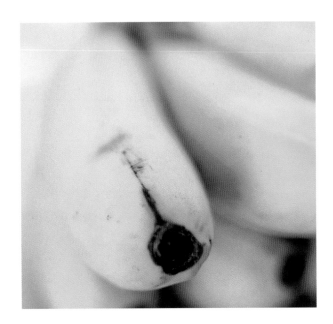

peanut power

This caramel-colored smoothie has a rich, naturally sweet taste. It's a good source of energy, with protein and calcium for strength and tissue-building.

Juice the apples. Peel the banana and blend with the apple and peanut butter until smooth. Pour into glasses, decorate the rim of the glasses with apple slices, and serve.

serves 1–2

$^1/_2$ sweet-fleshed
  pineapple
1 small red finger chile
3 oz/85 g watercress
$^1/_2$ lime with skin
$^1/_2$ ripe Hass avocado
sprigs of fresh
  watercress, to garnish

green zapper

This juice is very energizing, owing to the combination of sugars. A good source of beta-carotene and folic acid for strong growth and immunity, it cleanses the liver of toxins and aids digestion. Chile helps lower cholesterol and stimulates circulation.

Peel and quarter the pineapple. Halve the chile and seed. Juice the pineapple together with the watercress, lime, and chile. Scoop out the avocado flesh and blend with the juice until smooth. Pour into glasses, garnish with sprigs of watercress, and serve.

serves 1–2

1 orange
7 oz/200 g sweet potato
2 pears
2 Brazil nuts

just a sweetie

This delicious juice is packed with nutrients, particularly vitamins A, C, B6, and folic acid. Sweet potatoes and pears are low GI for slow-release energy to keep you going through a long day.

Peel the orange, leaving some of the white pith. Juice the sweet potato, pears, and orange. Pour into a glass, roughly chop the nuts, and sprinkle over the top to serve.

serves 1–2

1 pear
5$\frac{1}{2}$ oz/150 g blueberries
3$\frac{1}{2}$ oz/100 g soy yogurt
$\frac{1}{2}$ tsp agave syrup
2 tsp toasted slivered
   almonds

blueberry nectar

Blueberries are super-rich in antioxidants and help keep your brain healthy in later life. Agave is a low-GI natural sweetener that helps keep blood sugar levels constant. Yogurt and almonds provide calcium for bone strength.

Juice the pear and blueberries. Add the yogurt and agave syrup and whisk or blend until smooth and bubbly. Pour into a glass, sprinkle with the almonds, and serve.

uplifting

If it's hard to summon up the enthusiasm to enjoy life, a juicy pep-up will lift your spirits. The stress-busting ingredients can reduce blood pressure, increase energy levels, and cleanse the system. These antioxidant-rich juices will help you detox, boosting your levels of feel-good hormones, revitalizing your body and clearing your mind.

serves 1–2

1/2 small pineapple
3 oz/85 g blackberries
3 oz/85 g blueberries
1 tsp goji berries, roughly
  chopped

black 'n' blue

A good detoxing drink to cleanse the intestines and clear the sinuses, a general pep-up for a run-down system. All the berries, particularly the blueberries and goji berries, are very rich in disease-fighting, age-proofing antioxidants.

Cut the pineapple into chunks and juice with the blackberries and blueberries. Pour into a glass and sprinkle with the chopped goji berries to serve.

serves 1–2

2 scallions
3 tomatoes
1 oz/25 g fresh basil
1 garlic clove
ice cubes
shredded scallion, to
    garnish

tomato twister

A flavor-packed tomato-based juice that's a great source of beta-carotene and cancer-fighting lycopene. Basil calms the nerves and counteracts stress, and garlic is a good system cleanser and a natural antibiotic.

Trim the scallions. Place one tomato in the juicer and firmly pack in the scallions, basil, and garlic, then top with the remaining tomatoes. Juice all the ingredients, then pour into glasses with ice cubes. Top with shredded scallions and serve.

serves 1–2

$\frac{1}{2}$ Galia melon
3 celery stalks
4$\frac{1}{2}$ oz/125 g blackberries
1 kiwi

the reviver

Refreshing and rehydrating, cleansing and calming, and rich in vitamin C to boost the body's resistance, this juice is a perfect reviver after a hard day at the office.

Peel the melon and cut into chunks. Pack into the juicer with 1 celery stalk, the blackberries, and the kiwi. Juice all the ingredients together, then pour into glasses and serve with the remaining celery stalks to stir.

serves 1–2

¹/₂ iceberg lettuce
1 large carrot
¹/₄ oz/10 g fresh cilantro
3 radishes, with leaves
pepper
sprig of fresh cilantro
  and some carrot sticks,
  to garnish

carrot calmer

This calming juice is a good tonic for the digestive system, eyes and skin. It's also mildly diuretic and slightly sedative. Iceberg lettuce contains more natural calming substances than any other food and cilantro helps to reduce cholesterol.

Cut the lettuce into chunks and pack into the juicer with the carrot, cilantro, and radishes. Juice together, then pour into a glass. Sprinkle with pepper and add a sprig of cilantro and some carrot sticks to serve.

serves 1–2

5 fl oz/150 ml boiling
 water
1 ginseng tea bag or
 1 tsp ginseng tea
1 apple
1½ oz/40 g wild arugula
 leaves

stressbuster

A vibrant juice that helps liver and kidney function and prevents fluid retention.
Ginseng is a natural stimulant that helps to combat stress and lifts the mood.

Pour the boiling water over the tea bag or tea, and let stand for 4 minutes. Strain. Place the apple in the juicer and pack the arugula leaves firmly on top, then juice. Stir the juice into the tea, pour into glasses, and serve warm or cold.

serves 1–2

$^1/_2$ lemon
2 apples
3 oz/85 g pitted prunes
2 pears
freshly grated nutmeg

spiced fruit boost

Just the juice to give you a lift when you're flagging, it's packed with long-lasting energy, with good amounts of vitamin C and beta-carotene. Nutmeg is good for digestion, and is also an aphrodisiac!

Peel the lemon, leaving on a layer of white pith. Juice the apples, lemon, prunes, and pears together. Pour into glasses, sprinkle with grated nutmeg and serve.

serves 1–2

$1/2$ fennel bulb, with
  leaves
1 apple
1 carrot
1 small red bell pepper

red pep-up

Full of disease-fighting, anti-aging antioxidants, this drink provides lots of energy from natural sweetness and stimulants to help you get through the day.

Remove a few leaves from the fennel and reserve for garnish. Pack the fennel, apple, carrot, and bell pepper into the juicer and juice all the ingredients together. Pour into glasses, add a sprig of fennel leaves to each, and serve.

serves 1–2

6 apricots
1 orange
1 fresh lemongrass stalk
3/4-inch/2-cm piece of
  fresh ginger

apricot buzz

If your energy levels are low after lunch, this is the one to give you renewed vigor. It's rich in natural sugars, iron, potassium, and beta-carotene. Ginger speeds up the metabolic rate, lemongrass helps to relax the stomach, and both aid digestion.

Halve and pit the apricots. Peel the orange, leaving some of the white pith. Cut the lemongrass into chunks. Place the apricots, orange, lemongrass, and ginger in the juicer and juice all the ingredients together. Pour into glasses and serve.

serves 1–2

2 peaches
140 g/5 oz red grapes
4 oz/115 g strawberries
1 passion fruit
seeds from ¹/₂ vanilla
  bean

passionate magic

A great all-rounder for the system, packed with powerful antioxidants to slow down the signs of aging, as well as healing vitamins A and C. It also has mildly sedative, liver-cleansing, and anti-arthritic properties, from the phytochemicals in the fruits.

Halve and pit the peaches and juice with the grapes and strawberries. Halve the passion fruit and scoop out the flesh, scrape the seeds from the vanilla bean, and stir both into the juice. Pour into glasses and serve.

restoring

Whether you're fighting an infection or recovering from an injury, battling with pms or simply feeling tired, pour yourself a healing juice. If you have a cold, try a hot blackcurrant toddy packed with vitamin C and honey. Cure a hangover with a quick-fix juice to restore blood sugar levels and rehydrate the system.

serves 1–2

¹/₂ sweet pineapple
³/₄-inch/2-cm slice
   thin-skinned lemon
³/₄-inch/2-cm piece of
   fresh ginger

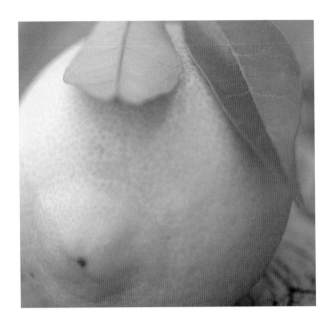

tummy soother

Pineapple juice is great for improving digestion and soothing an upset tummy.
The healing enzyme bromelin reduces bruising, so it can help with recovery from
an injury. It's also a good source of vitamin C, which helps to heal and fight
infection. Lemons are gently diuretic and help to cleanse the system.

Juice the pineapple, lemon, and ginger together, then pour
into glasses and serve.

serves 1–2

$1/4$ watermelon flesh, with
  seeds
$5^1/_2$ oz/150 g raspberries
ice cubes

red cooler

A great hangover cure, rehydrating, cleansing, and diuretic, and packed with vitamin C, which is depleted by alcohol. It also helps build the body's natural immunity, and the natural sugars will raise low blood sugar and revitalize you.

Juice the watermelon flesh with the raspberries. Pour into glasses over ice and serve.

serves 1–2

1 apple
7 oz/200 g blackcurrants
3$^1/_2$ fl oz/100 ml boiling
   water
1 tsp whipped honey,
   preferably Manuka

hot blackcurrant toddy

This comforting toddy is a great natural way to fight a sore throat, cold, or flu. Blackcurrants have four times the vitamin C of oranges. Manuka honey is very rich in vitamins and minerals and has powerful antibacterial properties.

Juice the apple with the blackcurrants. Add the honey to the boiling water and stir to dissolve, then stir in the juice. Pour into a glass and serve immediately.

serves 1–2
1 kiwi
1 apple
4 oz/115 g seedless
   white grapes

kiwi juice box

Sweet and energizing, this juice is packed with vitamin C. Grapes are good for restoring the body's alkaline balance and also a great cleanser, useful for detoxing and restoring healthy bowel movement.

Juice the kiwi and apple, then the grapes. Pour into glasses and serve just as it is, or pour over ice.

serves 1–2

1 white grapefruit
1 orange
1 kiwi
15 drops echinacea
   tincture
thinly pared twists of
   orange zest, to decorate

cold comforter

This is packed with vitamin C to fight colds and flu, with an added boost from echinacea, a powerful immune system booster that helps increase white blood cells to fight infection.

Peel the grapefruit and orange, leaving on some of the white pith. Juice the grapefruit, orange, and kiwi together. Stir in the echinacea drops and pour into glasses. Add a twist of orange zest to each and serve.

serves 1–2

1 orange
2 oz/55 g cranberries
1 banana
3^1/$_2$ oz/100 g soy yogurt
fine shreds of orange
   zest, to decorate

soothing smoothie

Cranberries are a good source of cancer-fighting phytochemicals, and are also soothing for the digestive and urinary tracts. This juice is packed with vitamin C, plus potassium for regulating blood pressure.

Peel the orange, leaving some of the white pith. Juice the orange and cranberries together. Add the peeled banana and yogurt, then blend until smooth. Pour into a glass, sprinkle with shreds of orange zest, and serve.

serves 1–2

7 oz/200 g pink forced
   rhubarb
1 orange
$3/4$-inch/2-cm piece fresh
   ginger
2 fl oz/50 ml soymilk
pinch of ground ginger,
   to decorate

pink ginger shake

A delicate pink juice that has valuable phytochemicals to boost the immune system and help repair tissues after injury. It's also good for regulating female hormones, and ginger can soothe digestive upsets.

Trim the rhubarb and cut into chunks. Peel the orange, leaving some of the white pith. Juice the rhubarb, orange, and ginger. Add the soymilk and shake or whisk to mix. Pour into a glass, sprinkle with ginger, and serve.

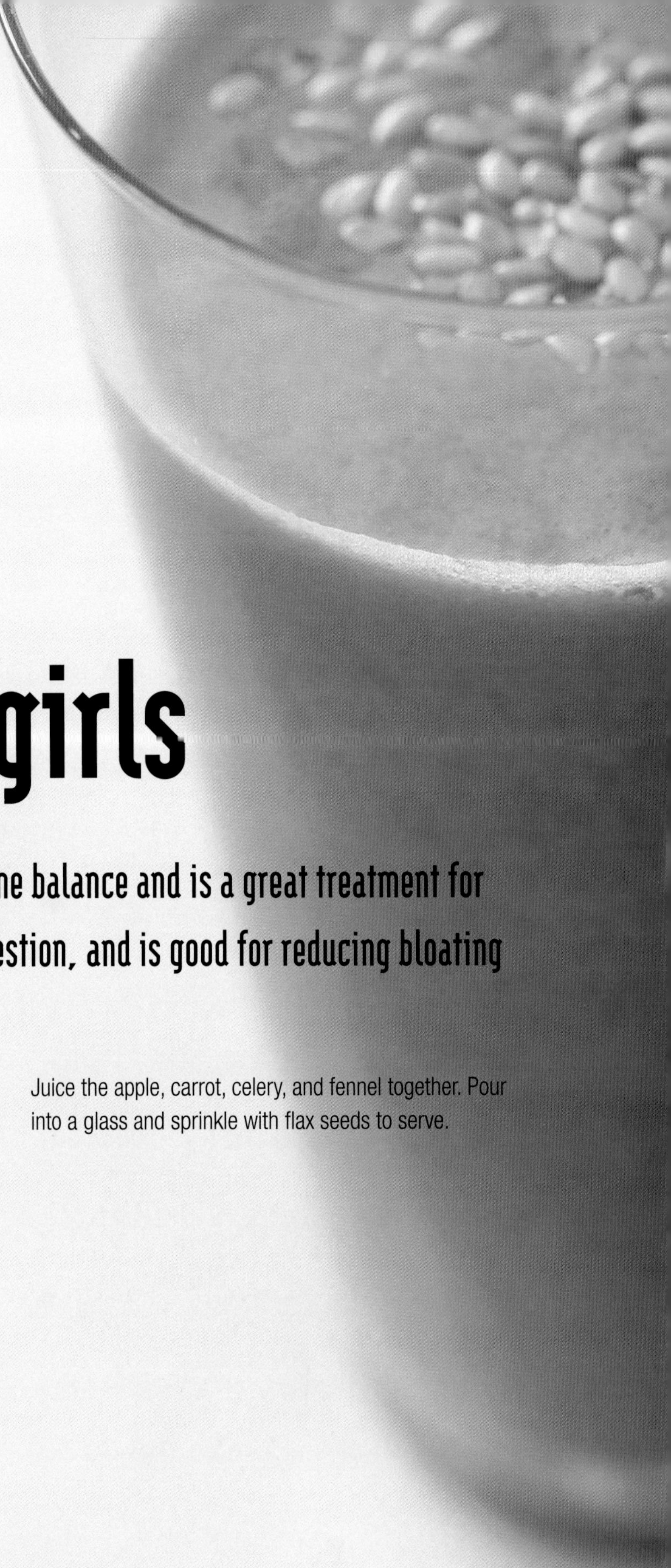

serves 1–2

1 apple
1 large carrot
1 celery stalk
$^1/_2$ fennel bulb
$^1/_2$ tsp flax seeds

one for the girls

This super juice promotes female hormone balance and is a great treatment for pms. It also has a calming effect on digestion, and is good for reducing bloating and flatulence.

Juice the apple, carrot, celery, and fennel together. Pour into a glass and sprinkle with flax seeds to serve.

serves 1–2

$^1/_2$ Galia melon
3 oz/85 g baby leaf
   spinach
2 large sprigs mint
2 large sprigs flat-leaf
   parsley
fresh mint sprigs, to
   decorate

green goddess

A cooling, cleansing drink, good for liver and kidney function, that helps lower cholesterol and relieves tension and insomnia. It's high in iron and in chlorophyll, which is good for the eyes and for maintaining healthy blood vessels.

Cut the outer hard rind from the melon, leaving the inner green layer, and cut into chunks. Pack half into the juicer, pack the spinach and herbs in firmly, then top with the remaining melon. Juice the ingredients then pour into glasses over ice. Add a sprig of mint to each and serve.